95 Phonics
Core Program™
Student Workbook

1d

475 Half Day Road, Suite 350
Lincolnshire, IL 60069
847-499-8200
www.95percentgroup.com

Written and published by
95 Percent Group Inc.
Susan L. Hall, EdD, Founder and Chief Executive Officer
475 Half Day Road, Suite 350
Lincolnshire, IL 60069
www.95percentgroup.com

Second Printing, 2021.

DAY 1

Sort Words

Word List				
1. ball	3. walk	5. rot	7. talk	9. stamp
2. poll	4. roll	6. hall	8. stall	10. troll

 all	oll	alk	NO
		chalk	fake

Sound-Spelling Mapping

1.

4.

2.

5.

3.

6.

Passage 1

A <u>Walk</u> to the Lake

1   Kate and Jake went on a <u>walk</u> to a lake. Kate's mom went on the
2   <u>walk</u> with them. Kate <u>called</u>, "Come on, Jake. Don't <u>balk</u>! I want to get to
3   the lake fast." Kate ran. Jake ran down a long path after Kate. They came
4   to a stone <u>wall</u>. Jake wanted to get over the <u>wall</u>, but it was too <u>tall</u>. He did
5   not want to <u>fall</u>. "That is not a <u>small</u> <u>wall</u>. Let's see if we can get past the <u>wall</u>
6   and not fall," said Jake.
7   The kids sprang into the tall grass, looking to get past the stone wall.
8   The grass was tall and they could not see where they were going. "I can't
9   find how to get to the lake," Kate said. "I think we are lost! Mom!" she
10   called. "Mom, Mom! Where are you?" Mom came strolling into the grass.
11   "I told you kids to walk to the lake and not run," she said. "You could
12   fall when you are running and roll down the hill into the lake."
13   "Let's all take a good stroll and talk," said Jake. "Please stop running."
14   They saw a small mink rolling and rolling in the grass. Jake said, "Let's
15   roll in the grass too!" Kate and Jake were rolling in the grass for a long time.
16   Mom said, "It's getting late. Let's walk back past the lake."
17   Kate, Jake, and Mom were talking as they were strolling home. Mom
18   said, "You all had a ball rolling and walking in the tall grass."

DAY 2

Pattern and Contrast Words

Word List				
1. came	3. stalk	5. chant	7. chalk	9. walk
2. stroll	4. toll	6. fall	8. stand	10. tall

all	oll	alk	NO
call			

Sound-Spelling Mapping

1. ☐☐☐☐

4. ☐☐☐

2. ☐☐

5. ☐☐

3. ☐☐

6. ☐☐☐☐

Lesson 24

 Read Passage – Passage 1
Go to page 180 and read *A Walk to the Lake*.

Written Response

Kate and Jake want
to roll in the grass like

DAY 3

Sound-Spelling Mapping with Student Phonics Chips

2 Sounds
all
oll
alk

m. all •

1.

2.

3.

4.

5.

Passage 2

To Make a Slate <u>Wall</u>

1   I want to <u>talk</u> to <u>all</u> of you on how to make a slate <u>wall</u>. Making a

2 <u>wall</u> is no <u>small</u> task and can take its <u>toll</u>. Use flat slate stones that are big

3 and <u>small</u>. Pile up <u>all</u> the slate for the <u>wall</u>. Use <u>chalk</u> to make the line as

4 long as you want. <u>Talk</u> over how long the <u>wall</u> will be.

5   Mix the bond and put it on the <u>chalk</u> line. Then, put the slate on the

6 bond. Roll the bond on top of all the slate and in the slits. If you stall, the

7 bond will get cold. The wall has a line of slate. How tall do you want the

8 wall to be? Put slate and bond to make the wall tall. Line up the wall

9 with the next line of slate. This will make the wall strong, so it will not fall.

10   Call two to three pals to stroll on by to see the wall. Have them walk

11 by and scan the wall for gaps.

12   You will have to stall crafting the wall to fill all the gaps with bond. To

13 make a tall wall, mix bond and put new slate on top.

14   How tall is the wall now? Stroll up to the wall. Is it still too small? Talk

15 with pals and take a poll to see if you want to stall. When you do stop, let

16 the bond set so the wall will stand for a long time.

DAY 4

Fluency: High-Frequency Words

has	fly	know	could
open	give	were	live
after	once	any	going
thank	from	put	round

Word Ladders

Sound Bank										
Consonants	b	c	f	g	h	m	p	r	t	w
Consonant Blends	dr	scr	sm	st	str	tr				
Consonant Digraphs	ch									

_all
wall
ball

_oll

_alk

DAY 5

Number of Sounds in High-Frequency Words

Word List	2 Sounds	3 Sounds	4 Sounds
1. went		let	
2. know			
3. little			
4. take			
5. white			
6. old			
7. walk			
8. open			

Fluency: Words

wall	stall	talk	malls
ball	troll	balk	chalk
stroll	small	call	toll
roll	gall	tall	scroll

Fluency: Phrases

get the chalk	know the troll	could be talking	when they walk
from the mall	take a stroll	roll the ball	down the hall
the tall pole	on the wall	the white chalk	after you talk
stall the call	go to the mall	thank the man	scan the wall

Sentence Dictation

1.

2.

3.

📄 **Read Passage – Passage 1**   Go to page 180 and read *A Walk to the Lake*.

1. What stopped Jake from getting over the wall?

2. Did Kate, Jake, and Mom have fun on the walk? How do you know?

📄 **Read Passage – Passage 2**   Go to page 183 and read *To Make a Slate Wall*.

1. What makes the stone wall strong?

2. How can pals help with making a slate stone wall?

DAY 1
Sort Words

Word List					
1. long	3. spring	5. span	7. sank	9. pick	11. think
2. conk	4. bang	6. honk	8. pink	10. fling	12. strong

ang	ing	ong
sprang		

ank	ink	onk	NO
thank			

Sound-Spelling Mapping

s	t	r	ing	

1.

2.

3.

4.

5.

6.

Morphology: Ending -ed

Rule	Verb	Verb + ed	Spelling Rules
1	fish	fished	Verb spelled with a **vowel team**, **ends in y**, or has **2 consonants at the end**, add -ed.
2	bake	baked	Verb spelled with the **silent-e pattern, drop the last e** before adding -ed.
3	tap	tapped	Verb spelled with a **single vowel followed by 1 consonant**, the final **consonant is doubled** before adding -ed.

Verb	Rule	Verb + ed
wish	1	wished
1. time		
2. lock		
3. cup		
4. like		
5. pet		

Passage 1

A <u>Walk</u> in the <u>Mall</u>

1   I was sitting at home one <u>spring</u> on my sunlit deck. <u>All</u> of a sudden

2   there was a shrill <u>ring</u>. I <u>sprang</u> up to grab the <u>call</u>. It was my Gram asking

3   if I wanted to take a <u>walk</u> at the <u>mall</u>. I was <u>sold</u> on taking a <u>stroll</u>. When

4   Gram came to pick me up, I was <u>bold</u> and asked if she <u>minds</u> if I <u>bring</u>

5   my <u>chalk</u>, a <u>ball</u>, and my dog <u>Colt</u>. She said, "That is fine. Pack up those

6   <u>things</u>, and let's go." She drove us to the <u>mall</u>. In the <u>hall</u> of the <u>mall</u>,

7   we <u>walked</u> past <u>stalls</u> <u>linked</u> side by side with <u>bling</u> and <u>stalls</u> with <u>string</u>

8   and <u>bolts</u>.

9   We <u>strolled</u> the <u>long</u> <u>mall</u> path and came to a spot where a man was

10   <u>talking</u> on the theme of <u>chalk</u> crafts. My Gram and I <u>stalled</u> to watch. When I

11   was done, we kept <u>walking</u> to <u>find</u> some grass. I let <u>Colt</u> run, <u>roll</u>, and chase

12   the <u>ball</u>. He had a <u>wild</u> time <u>finding</u> the <u>ball</u> and <u>bringing</u> it back to me.

13   Gram said, "I <u>think</u> it is time to take a <u>small</u> rest. Let's stop and <u>find</u> a

14   <u>cold</u> <u>drink</u>." Then, we <u>sank</u> down on the bench on the <u>wall</u> of the <u>mall</u>. We

15   <u>drank</u> our <u>cold</u> cans of pop and then <u>strolled</u> to the end of the <u>mall</u>. The

16   sun was <u>sinking</u>, and our <u>stroll</u> was over in a <u>blink</u>. I <u>thanked</u> my <u>kind</u> Gram

17   and <u>told</u> her I had the <u>most</u> fun <u>talking</u> and <u>walking</u> with her.

Lesson
25

DAY 2

Sort Words

Word List		
1. talk	5. told	9. host
2. hold	6. stall	10. dill
3. bolt	7. post	11. roll
4. hole	8. stroll	12. ball

old	olt	ost
	jolt	

oll	all	alk	NO

Writing: Contractions

2 Words	Combine Words and Slash	Contraction
do not	don∅t	don't
1. can not		
2. let us		
3. I am		
4. it is		
5. is not		

DAY 3 Pattern and Contrast Words

Word List			
1. bind	3. chill	5. wild	7. fine
2. mild	4. grin	6. grind	8. find

ild	ind	NO
child		

Sound-Spelling Mapping with Student Phonics Chips

2 Sounds	3 Sounds
ang, ing, ong alk, all, oll old, olt	ank, ink, onk ild, ind ost

1.

2.

3.

4.

5.

6.

192   95 Phonics Core Program™ • Grade 1 • Student Workbook   Copyright © 2020, 95 Percent Group Inc. All rights reserved.

DAY 4

Syllable Mapping

First Syllable	Second Syllable	Multisyllable Words
dis	miss	dismiss
1.		
2.		
3.		
4.		
5.		

Passage 2

The Game of <u>Pall</u> <u>Mall</u>

1   When you <u>think</u> of a <u>mall,</u> what comes to <u>mind</u>? Shops lined up on

2   both sides of a <u>walking</u> path with benches? That is one <u>kind</u> of <u>mall</u>. In the

3   past, there was a game <u>called</u> <u>Pall</u> <u>Mall</u> that was from the French.

4   At that time, the game was for men who had the <u>most</u> <u>gold</u>.

5   The game was played with a mallet and some <u>balls</u>. To set up the

6   game, <u>all</u> the men met at one end of a <u>long</u> lane. The object was to get

7   the <u>ball</u> in the <u>small</u> hole at the distant end of the lane. To get the <u>ball</u>

8   there, a man had to <u>hold</u> a stick <u>called</u> a mallet, <u>wind</u> up, and take a

9   strong, <u>bold</u> <u>swing</u> at the <u>ball</u> with the mallet. After the hit, the man <u>walked</u>

10   to the <u>ball</u> and hit it again. Every shot was <u>linked</u>. While <u>walking</u>, there was

11   often a lot of <u>talking</u> going on. This made the <u>Pall</u> <u>Mall</u> game fun as the

12   men <u>scolded</u> in jest and made comments on the <u>swings</u>. When <u>all</u> the <u>balls</u>

13   got close to the hole, the <u>ball</u> was hit with <u>small</u>, <u>mild</u> strokes to push it

14   in the hole.

15   <u>Pall</u> <u>Mall</u> is <u>long</u> gone, but there is a game that comes to <u>mind</u>.

16   Can you <u>think</u> of it? Here is a hint. It is played with clubs and <u>balls</u> on <u>long</u>

17   paths of grass.

DAY 5

Sentence Writing

Word Bank				
game	bring	long	wild	basket
sink	fun	bonk	walk	bolt
rank	most	bang	ball	racket

_____

- -

_____

- -

_____

Word Building

Syllable Bank	
First Syllable	**Second Syllable**
in	dog
home	bone
hot	shine
wish	side
cup	cake
lip	stick
sun	made

Multisyllable Words
wishbone
1.
2.
3.

Lesson 25

Fluency: Phrases

on the tank	the wild child	under the sink	just a ring
with a bang	over the gold	a long walk	for the kind host
on a roll	in the bank	from the song	with a jolt
with the king	at the fling	into the wild	hang the blinds

Sentence Dictation

1.

2.

3.

Read Passage – Passage 2   Go to page 194 and read *The Game of Pall Mall*.

1. Can you think of a game that is like Pall Mall? How are they the same?

DAY 1

Sort Words

Word List			
1. free	4. foe	7. toast	10. bright
2. toe	5. right	8. coach	
3. grand	6. sheet	9. stove	

ee	igh	oa	oe	NO
	night	foam		

Sound-Spelling Mapping

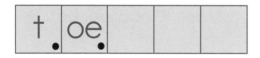

t	oe			

1.

4.

2.

5.

3.

6.

Passage 1

<u>Doe</u> the <u>Goat</u> and Kids

1   <u>Doe</u> the <u>Goat</u> had <u>three</u> kids. Her kids were <u>Dee</u>, <u>Joe</u>, and <u>Moe</u>. <u>Doe</u> and

2   her kids lived <u>high</u> on the hill. They liked to play <u>fight</u> and be funny till <u>night</u>. One

3   spring, <u>Doe</u> said, "Kids, let's go to the <u>creek</u> down by the <u>green</u> <u>tree</u> and play."

4   <u>Dee</u>, <u>Joe</u>, and <u>Moe</u> were <u>keen</u> on going to the <u>creek</u>.

5   On the trip to the <u>creek</u>, they <u>see</u> some <u>sheep</u> who were <u>seeking</u> help.

6   One sheep had her feet stuck deep in the mud. Dee let out a sigh and said, "I will

7   help the sheep free her feet." Dee went to the sheep and gave a slight tug. She

8   freed the sheep's feet! Doe, Joe, and Moe were glad for Dee. Dee had helped

9   the sheep to be free.

10   Doe and her kids made it down to the creek by the green tree. They

11   played by the side of the creek and roamed down by a boat. Doe told them

12   to keep away from the boat. The goats moaned and groaned.

13   The goats left the boat to play fight. The goats were jumping and kicking

14   up high. Doe said, "Let's go! It is going to be night soon and time to roam back

15   to home." Moe, Dee, and Joe ran up the hill on fast feet "Good job, kids! You

16   have feet that are so fast and fleet!"

17   When they made it up the high hill, Doe locked the home up tight and

18   the goats all went into a deep sleep.

DAY 2

Pattern and Contrast Words

Word List			
1. goal	4. doe	7. flight	10. loan
2. spell	5. loaf	8. Moe	11. speed
3. feel	6. green	9. gold	12. mole

ee	igh	oa	oe	NO
	light			

Sound-Spelling Mapping

1.

2.

3.

4.

5.

6.

Lesson 26

📄 **Read Passage – Passage 1**   Go to page 198 and read *Doe the Goat and Kids*.

Doe, Dee, Joe, and
Moe went down to
the _____ to
play.

DAY 3

Sound-Spelling Mapping

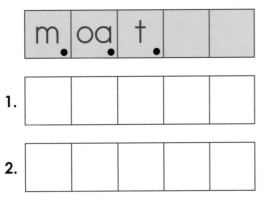

1. ⬜⬜⬜⬜⬜

2. ⬜⬜⬜⬜⬜

3. ⬜⬜⬜⬜⬜

4. ⬜⬜⬜⬜⬜

5. ⬜⬜⬜⬜⬜

6. ⬜⬜⬜⬜⬜

Passage 2

Keep Loads of Luck

1   What might be the same with an oak tree seed, a cat, and the right

2   feet of rabbits? They all boast to bring loads of luck and riches and to

3   mend woes! Do you keep any trinkets for good luck?

4   You may have seen, from the street, the small plastic cat that peeks

5   and waves at you from a shop. You might see these cats in red, white,

6   green, and mixed shades. The hand of the small cat goes up and down.

7   If the left hand is sighted up, it is said to bring good fate and keep away

8   foes. If the right hand is seen up, expect loads of riches.

9   You might not know that seeds from some oak trees are good luck.

10   The seed stands for might. These oak tree seeds are sighted in weddings

11   and on TV. The oak tree seeds are a high prize of luck for some. For good

12   luck, some Brits keep the seeds in pockets.

13   Last, the most known trinket of luck is the right feet of rabbits. It

14   might give you the creeps, but it is said that the back, right heel of a rabbit

15   holds the fate to the goals you seek. You can hold on tight to one at night

16   for a deep sleep.

17   Do you have fun things you keep to seek good luck? Next time you

18   roam to a new spot, bring one of these good luck tokens with you. It is fun

19   to trade a bit of good luck with those you meet. In time, you might know

20   lots of things to help you seek a life of luck if the funny tales are right!

DAY 4

Fluency: High-Frequency Words

every	from	put	over
again	live	know	once
open	has	give	thank
how	after	any	going

Word Building

Sound Bank							
Vowel Teams	ee	igh	oa	oe			
Initial Consonants	b	c	f	l	r	s	t
Initial Blends	cr	fl	str				
Final Consonants	p	t					

b ee t

1.

2.

3.

4.

5.

DAY 5   Fluency: Words

toe	wheel	light	street
slight	throat	creek	tight
goal	sweet	float	fright
foe	bright	woe	coach

Fluency: Phrases

into the creek	float the boat	brush my teeth	see the light
the right street	feel the sheep	a sweet sigh	go to sleep
from the boat	under the hoe	on the street	going to the coast
have some toast	meet and greet	some sweet cake	jump for joy

Sentence Dictation

1.

2.

3.

Read Passage – Passage 1

Go to page 198 and read *Doe the Goat and Kids*.

1. Where did Doe and her kids live?

_____

_____

_____

_____

2. What did Dee do to free the sheep?

_____

_____

_____

_____

 ## Read Passage – Passage 2

Go to page 201 and read *Keep Loads of Luck*.

1. What three things might bring good luck?

_____

_____

_____

_____

2. Where are the oak seeds kept to bring good luck?

_____

_____

_____

_____

DAY 1

Sort Words

Word List			
1. braid	4. clay	7. coin	10. law
2. haunt	5. main	8. fraud	
3. gray	6. claw	9. toy	

ai	ay	oi	oy	au	aw
		boil	boy		

Sound-Spelling Mapping

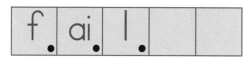

1.

2.

3.

4.

5.

6.

Passage 1

The <u>Claim</u> on <u>Gray</u> Lake

1   The big <u>day</u> was here, and the sun was <u>launching</u> up at <u>dawn</u>! Gram was

2   <u>hauling</u> the boat on the back of the truck. We were on our <u>way</u> to <u>Gray</u> Lake for

3   a <u>day</u> of fishing that we hoped to <u>claim</u> as one of our best.

4   At the lake, Gram and <u>May</u> drove to the boat <u>launch</u>. <u>Gail</u> and <u>Craig</u> ran

5   the <u>trail</u> to the end of the <u>launch</u> and <u>waited</u> for the boat. When the boat was

6   on its way down the launch, May tossed the rope to Craig. Gram said, "Draw it

7   up to the dock and keep the rope tight."

8   Gail crawled in the boat with the pail of bait. Craig held the rope tight

9   waiting for Gram. Craig was the last to crawl in, drawing the rope in to set the

10 boat free to launch. Gram aimed way left, crawling in the shade by the rocks where

11 we could haul in the fish.

12 One by one, we launched a baited line into the lake and waited to get a

13 bite. The main goal was to draw in the biggest fish of the day and claim bragging

14 rights. We all wait as Craig taunted the fish with his bait.

15 May had just laid back with a big yawn when she felt a tug. "Whoa!" she

16 yelled, grabbing her pole and making the boat sway. May was fighting to raise

17 the big fish when the line snapped! Craig and Gail hauled the fish up with the net

18 just in time! Gram saw it and gave praise for hauling it in! We all could lay claim

19 to the biggest fish at Gray Lake. We smiled and boasted as Gram aimed her way

20 back to the boat launch.

DAY 2

Pattern and Contrast Words

Word List					
1. chain	3. soil	5. straw	7. fault	9. join	11. draw
2. joy	4. day	6. play	8. soy	10. plane	12. sold

ai 	ay	oi	oy
drain			

au	aw	(NO)

Sound-Spelling Mapping

w.	ai.	t.	

1.

2.

3.

4.

5.

6.

Read Passage – Passage 1

Go to page 206 and read *The Claim on Gray Lake*.

DAY 3

Sound-Spelling Mapping

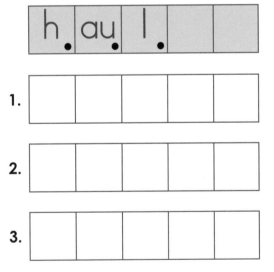

1.

2.

3.

4.

5.

6.

Passage 2

Queen <u>Fay</u>'s Foal

1   Dad said <u>Joy</u> and I could <u>join</u> him to see Queen <u>Fay</u>'s foal. The <u>wait</u> had come

2 to an end, and Queen <u>Fay</u>'s new foal was on its <u>way</u>. Dad said most foals come at

3 night so we had the <u>day</u> to help him. We could <u>aid</u> in making a new bed of <u>straw</u>

4 over the <u>moist</u> <u>soil</u>.

5   Dad told <u>Joy</u> and me that he <u>saw</u> Queen <u>Fay</u> did not eat <u>grain</u> and <u>soy</u> in her

6 pail at dawn. He saw that she looked taut and was feeling some pain. He was saying

7 how she swayed in her stall. Then as we hauled straw, he looked at the daunting sky.

8 Dad said, "We need to haul this straw in as rain is coming."

9   Joy and I saw Dad wipe Fay and pin her tail. He then led her to stay on the

10 fresh straw and draped her with a shawl. Joy and I hauled in a pail of grain. Queen

11 Fay strained a bit, moaned, and got up but then coiled back down. Just as the rain

12 and hail came, we all yawned from the long day.

13   The time had come. Queen Fay lay down and mauled the straw as she

14 strained. We saw two feet. I looked at Joy and my jaw dropped as Queen Fay

15 strained again! Dad helped Queen Fay have her foal. Dad hoisted the foal up so he

16 could draw it close to Queen Fay. Dad smiled while saying, "It's a boy!" We saw the

17 gaunt foal draw up his legs again and again. Then the foal was on his feet. Joy and

18 I saw Queen Fay lick the new foal like she wanted to flaunt that he had no flaws. It

19 was a good day for Dad and Queen Fay!

Lesson
27

DAY 4

Fluency: High-Frequency Words

went	what	walk	who
away	down	where	pretty
could	how	them	think
want	was	when	any

Word Building

Sound Bank							
Vowel Teams	ai	ay	oi	oy	au	aw	
Initial Consonants	b	c	f	h	r	s	t
Initial Blends	br	cr	fl				
Final Consonants	l	n					

b oi l

1.

2.

3.

4.

5.

DAY 5   Fluency: Words

chain	hay	coin	boy
fault	quail	brain	spray
play	draw	straw	fail
day	claw	toy	waist

Fluency: Phrases

she saw Roy	see the quail	what is the law	it's a train
play in the straw	fly by the bay	paint with Joy	like to draw
ask for the mail	could be his fault	on his claw	going to rain
the bright coin	the day after	going to launch	in the clay

Sentence Dictation

1. _____

2. _____

3. _____

Read Passage – Passage 1

Go to page 206 and read *The Claim on Gray Lake*.

1. Where are they going fishing?

2. Who went fishing?

Read Passage – Passage 2

Go to page 209 and read *Queen Fay's Foal*.

1. What is Queen Fay's bed made of?

2. What made the kids glad they stayed?

DAY 1

Sort Words

Word List			
1. now	4. flight	7. sweat	10. treat
2. grow	5. seat	8. shape	
3. bread	6. brown	9. flown	

ea 	ea	ow	ow	NO
clean		blow		

Sound-Spelling Mapping

h	ea	d		

1.

2.

3.

4.

5.

6.

Passage 1

Growing a Lean, Mean Team

1   Running is <u>how</u> I get fit, but it can be a <u>real</u> <u>beast</u>! I think of the <u>heat</u> and
2 cold with <u>dread</u>. <u>How</u> I <u>dread</u> running in the <u>heat</u>! I <u>reach</u> for things <u>meant</u> for sun
3 and not for <u>snow</u>. The <u>sweat</u> <u>beads</u> up and runs <u>down</u> my <u>head</u> and <u>brow</u>. Running
4 in the <u>heat</u> can <u>leave</u> me in a <u>real</u> <u>heap</u>. Yet when the <u>snow</u> comes <u>down</u> in the
5 cold, I hope for a <u>sweat</u>!

6   Now I plan meals meant for running. I chow down on meals with a spread
7 of lean meats and breads shown to reap what I need to run the next day. On days
8 when I plan a long run, I frown on eating a meal. If I eat and run, I might not
9 feel well.

10   I now run with a team that vows to stay lean and in good shape. When we
11 head out to run each day, we run on town roads and tread the town paths. We
12 run with ease on roads. Some days we run down on the beach. Running on sand is
13 slow and without ease. When running in sand, that deep tread makes me growl!
14 We now have grown a lean, mean running team on the prowl for a win.

15   Once, running meant just fun to me. It was a sneak peek at what real
16 runners do. Now when I run, I vow to reach a goal. When that goal is reached, I
17 feel I own it and beam with pride. Running has grown to be the thread in my life
18 that reaps joy.

DAY 2

Pattern and Contrast Words

Word List			
1. show	4. blow	7. head	10. mow
2. sprout	5. now	8. team	11. spread
3. leap	6. frown	9. how	12. teeth

ea	ea	ow	ow	NO
least				

Sound-Spelling Mapping

1. [ ][ ][ ][ ][ ]   4. [ ][ ][ ][ ][ ]

2. [ ][ ][ ][ ][ ]   5. [ ][ ][ ][ ][ ]

3. [ ][ ][ ][ ][ ]   6. [ ][ ][ ][ ][ ]

Lesson 28

 Read Passage – Passage 1

Go to page 214 and read *Growing a Lean, Mean Team*.

Running in the heat
leaves a runner

DAY 3

Sound-Spelling Mapping

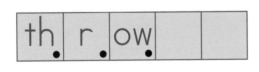

| th | r | ow | | |

1.

4.

2.

5.

3.

6.

Passage 2

<u>Beaches</u> and <u>Peaks</u> of Spain

1   If you could <u>stow</u> away on a boat, where might you <u>sneak</u> off to? Do you

2 <u>dream</u> of <u>towns</u> and <u>crowds</u> and the <u>glow</u> of sun on a <u>beach</u>? Do you like <u>snow</u>

3 and high <u>peak</u> trails that <u>spread</u> for miles? If so, Spain is the <u>dream</u> trip for you.

4   In the past, when men <u>rowed</u> up and <u>breached</u> the <u>beaches</u> of the

5 land <u>now</u> called Spain, they yelled "Span, span!" This <u>meant</u> "hare," which

6 led to the naming of Spain. The hare ran wild and chowed on the lush lands

7 heaped with plants and grown trees.

8   Spain has glowing beaches and high peaks with snow. If you leave at

9 dawn when the sun shows, you can beat the heat and reach the peaks of

10 snow. Then, head to the beach when the sun is low and the day reaches dusk.

11   A trip to Spain is a real treat! The crowds that like to hike and bike can

12 go on trails that lead to the peaks. They tread up to reach the top and gaze

13 down at the sea. Other crowds are pleased by gleaming gold sand beaches,

14 which seem fresh and clean and good for the health. You must not leave

15 Spain without seeing the sight of a black sand beach, which will raise an eye

16 brow. It is a treat to see but holds too much heat to stay long.

17   The meals in Spain are meant to please. You will chow down on lots of

18 beans, meat, and bread. Some dread clams and crab from the sea, but if you

19 like them then you must head to Spain to eat.

20   This was just a sneak peek of a dream trip to Spain with a pleasing life

21 by the sea!

DAY 4

Fluency: High-Frequency Words

any	good	once	could
our	what	fly	were
when	after	some	give
from	every	know	again

Word Building

Sound Bank							
Vowel Teams	ea	ow					
Initial Consonants	b	c	h	l	m	r	s
Initial Blends	br	fr					
Final Consonants	d	l	n				

h | ow | l

1.

2.

3.

4.

5.

DAY 5   Fluency: Words

throw	bread	cow	low
health	clown	seat	frown
blow	least	meat	breath
flow	row	crow	treat

Fluency: Phrases

like a peach	at the show	to his health	as it grows
into the snow	in a sweat	on its own	eat a treat
like a cow	hit my head	the whale blows	where is the bead
on the row	in the know	with the bread	for the crown

Sentence Dictation

1. _____

2. _____

3. _____

Read Passage – Passage 1

Go to page 214 and read *Growing a Lean, Mean Team*.

1. What might make you not feel well on a run?

2. "Deep tread makes me growl!" What is "deep tread"?

Read Passage – Passage 2

Go to page 217 and read *Beaches and Peaks of Spain*.

1. What are the best sights to see in Spain?

2. How do the peaks and beaches look in Spain?

DAY 1

Sort Words

Word List			
1. honk	4. grill	7. form	10. march
2. mark	5. verb	8. blur	11. prop
3. horn	6. park	9. from	12. third

ar	or	er ir ur	NO
	fork	girl	

Sound-Spelling Mapping

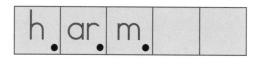

1.

4.

2.

5.

3.

6.

Passage 1

The Hard Day

1   My name is Amber, and it was a hard day. To start, I burned my

2   toast. Then, Dad's car did not start so I had to walk far to class. When I

3   turned by the park, a big storm started. I ran to my first class in a rain storm.

4   I was late, so I could not play turf ball with my pal Marco.

5   My teacher Miss Stark asked for the form for our class trip to the art

6   show. My form was torn and wet from the storm. Miss Stark said I could not

7   go. For the first time, I did not get to go to the art show with the class. I had

8   to wait in a third grade class for the rest of the time.

9   At lunch, Carter poked me with a hot, sharp fork. The fork burned

10   my arm. Carter did not seem sad for hurting me. After lunch while playing

11   turf ball, I stepped on a hard thorn and it tore my sock.

12   Mom told me some days are just hard. She said, "Try not to harp on

13   the bad parts. You have a new start in the morning. If you keep marching

14   on, it will soon be a blur."

15   Mom is so smart. When I need her, she perks me up. I curled up on

16   the porch with her and smiled. It was a hard day, but I was glad for a fresh

17   start in the morning.

Lesson
29

DAY 2

Pattern and Contrast Words

Word List			
1. dark	4. cord	7. spring	10. thorn
2. herd	5. card	8. fur	11. hard
3. gripe	6. chirp	9. star	12. sworn

ar 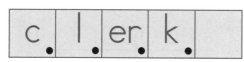	or	er ir ur	NO
		curb	

Sound-Spelling Mapping

c	l	er	k

1.

2.

3.

4.

5.

6.

Lesson 29

 Read Passage – Passage 1 Go to page 222 and read *The Hard Day*.

The car did not start, so Amber had to

DAY 3

Multisyllable Word Building

Syllable Bank					
Vowel-r Syllables			Other Syllables		
/ar/	/or/	/er/	Closed		Vowel Team
star	port	bird	black	sun	rain
	storm	burn	fish	wind	sea
			ship		snow

sea + port = seaport

1. _____ + _____ = _____

2. _____ + _____ = _____

3. _____ + _____ = _____

4. _____ + _____ = _____

5. _____ + _____ = _____

Passage 2

Corn Husk Dolls

1   Have you seen tall <u>corn</u> growing at a <u>farm</u>? The <u>part</u> of the

2   <u>corncob</u> we eat is <u>under</u> long, green leaves. Some may <u>discard</u> this

3   <u>part</u> <u>after</u> <u>harvest</u>. The <u>first</u> <u>farmers</u> liked to use all <u>parts</u> of the <u>corncob</u>.

4   This is how the <u>corn</u> husk doll was <u>first</u> <u>born</u>. <u>Corn</u> husk dolls <u>are</u> made

5   from the old leaves <u>or</u> husks of a <u>corncob</u>. The <u>art</u> of making dolls from

6   the firm husk of corn is not new. The charm of this art form comes from

7   far back in time.

8   It is not hard to make a corn husk doll. All you need is five corn

9   husks and yarn. First, soak the hard corn husks. Do not skip this part.

10 The husks will be too hard to form. Next, stack four of the corn husks.

11 The sharp parts must all be turned up. Now, make a bow with a short

12 strand of yarn one inch down. Turn the husks and put the long ends

13 over the yarn. This will form the head of the doll.

14 Next, curl up the last corn husk. To make the arms, use a bow

15 with yarn. Slide the arm part under the long end of the doll. Now,

16 mold more yarn under the arms. To make the arms short, trim the ends.

17 Twirl the husks to hide the yarn. Swirl the end parts to form her skirt. For

18 pants, cut the corn husk up to the yarn. Make a bow of yarn at each

19 end. With the yarn, you can make a shirt for the doll.

20 The first corn husk dolls had charm. One perk of making corn

21 husk dolls is selling them at craft shows. This short craft can be a real

22 fun form of art.

Lesson 29

DAY 4

Fluency: Multisyllable Words

sunset	basket	contest	cactus	dislike
sister	farmer	forgave	stargaze	pattern

DAY 5

Sort Syllables

Word	Closed	Vowel Team	Vowel-r
el|bow	el	bow	
1. summer			
2. winter			
3. window			
4. oatmeal			
5. carpet			
6. turnip			
7. corner			
8. impact			

Fluency: Phrases

see the bird	plant a fern	on the shirt	under the porch
made me twirl	on the farm	get the fork	after the storm
on the chart	find the clerk	blow the horn	the burn hurt
sort the socks	at the barn	play some cards	born to be smart

Sentence Writing

Word Bank			
hard	storm	squirt	first
hurt	yard	girl	new
teacher	summer	could	going

1. _____

_____

_____

2. _____

_____

_____

Lesson 29

Read Passage – Passage 1
Go to page 222 and read *The Hard Day*.

1. What are 2 things that made Amber have a hard day?

_____

- -

_____

- -

_____

2. What made Amber's arm burn?

_____

- -

_____

_____

- -

_____

Read Passage – Passage 2
Go to page 225 and read *Corn Husk Dolls*.

1. Where is the part of the corn that we eat?

_____

- -

_____

_____

- -

_____

2. What do you need to make corn husk dolls?

_____

- -

_____

_____

- -

_____

DAY 1

Multisyllable Routine

s<u>u</u>b	j<u>e</u>ct
1. t e n n i s
2. m a g n e t
3. h e l m e t
4. u n t i l
5. h i d d e n
6. i n d e x
7. f i t n e s s
8. d e n t i s t

Syllable Mapping

sun	set
1.	
2.	
3.	
4.	
5.	
6.	

Passage 1

The <u>Rascal</u>

1   <u>Justin</u> and I went to <u>Griffin's</u> home to plant seeds in his yard. We hoped to

2 have a <u>picnic</u> after that. <u>Griffin</u> had just locked <u>Bandit's</u> leash to the <u>sundeck</u>.

3 <u>Bandit</u>, <u>Griffin's</u> <u>basset</u> dog, <u>often</u> finds <u>problems</u>. I asked <u>Griffin</u> what <u>Bandit</u> did

4 to be stuck on the <u>sundeck</u>. He pointed to piles of messed up soil in his yard. He

5 looked up at the <u>frantic</u> dog and said, "I think the hound dug that hole in the dirt.

6 <u>Bandit</u> has dirt all over the yard and me, too!"

7   We went to work planting seeds. "See that?" Griffin said as he pointed to a

8 ripped seed packet. We stopped planting to check out the problem. The seeds

9 were in a pile. "Griffin, you have to admit this is not Bandit's work," Justin said.

10 "We can dismiss Bandit as the rascal."

11   "See this hole next to the seed packet?" I asked. "What could be in that

12 tunnel?" Griffin was going to find what was hidden there. All of a sudden, he

13 rushed into the shed. He was missing for a short time, and then came back with a

14 wire box. Griffin said not to be upset. It was a box to trap the rascal. Griffin's plan

15 was to catch the rascal and set him free, far away from the plants.

16   We put walnuts in the box to set a trap for the rascal. We undid Bandit's

17 leash and went inside to wait. After a short time, Griffin looked and said, "We got

18 him!" The rascal turned out to be a chipmunk! He was cute, but Griffin said he

19 was a problem and had to go. Justin set the chipmunk free. At last, we can enjoy

20 our picnic!

DAY 2
Sort Syllables

Divide Syllables	Closed	Closed	Silent-e	Vowel Team	Vowel-r
cat|nap	cat	nap			
1. sudden					
2. admit					
3. person					
4. hammock					
5. update					
6. upper					
7. sunray					
8. uphill					

Syllable Mapping

pub	lic

1. | | |
|---|---|

2. | | |
|---|---|

3. | | |
|---|---|

4. | | |
|---|---|

5. | | |
|---|---|

6. | | |
|---|---|

📄 Read Passage – Passage 1   Go to page 230 and read *The Rascal*.

Griffin used
in the box to trap the

DAY 3
Multisyllable Word Building

First Syllable	
nap	bath
up	back
in	sun
fit	hot
chip	pic

Second Syllable	
hill	kin
tub	munk
side	nic
ness	set
dog	pack

nap **+** kin **=** napkin

1. _____ **+** _____ **=** _____

2. _____ **+** _____ **=** _____

3. _____ **+** _____ **=** _____

4. _____ **+** _____ **=** _____

Passage 2

Sundecks

1   A <u>sundeck</u> is a spot to lay in the sun and let the <u>sunrays</u> warm the skin.

2   All <u>sundecks</u> are <u>sunlit</u> and can be found on the <u>upper</u> deck of a ship, on a

3   boat, or at a home. At home, in a boat, or on a ship, you can have a <u>picnic</u>

4   on a <u>sundeck</u>. It is a <u>perfect</u> spot to eat lunch or <u>dinner</u>. At home, you can

5   <u>invite</u> pals to a <u>picnic</u>.

6   A <u>sundeck</u> on the top deck of a ship can go round the <u>entire</u> <u>upper</u>

7   deck. If the ship is big, there are spots for lots of chairs and hammocks to lay

8   upon in the sun. There are plastic chairs and cloth hammocks on sundecks

9   for the crowd to enjoy the sunrays. There are also rustic chairs and hammocks

10   too. It is safe to rest on a sundeck when the ship is under way.

11   Small boats have sundecks too. The best spot for a sundeck on a little

12   boat is at the rear. The small size of the boat means the sundeck has a spot

13   for just one person at a time.

14   A sundeck can be part of a home. It's like a porch at the back of a

15   home. If the sundeck is old and dark, you can update it with some pastel

16   paint or fresh stain. You might put plastic chairs and a hammock there too.

17   In the winter, a sundeck is still fun to warm up in the sun, but sundecks

18   are used most often in the fall, spring, and summer. Keep a basket of cream

19   to get a suntan and not a sunburn. If you have a sundeck, you will want to

20   enjoy the sunrays with pals.

Lesson
30

DAY 4

Fluency: High-Frequency Words

too	thank	put	said
have	how	know	once
give	round	please	open
again	pretty	live	well

Word Chains

unkind
until
unwell
unpack

DAY 5

Read Words and Sort Syllables

Divide Syllables	Closed	Closed	Silent-e	Vowel Team
z<u>i</u>g | z<u>a</u>g	zig	zag		
1. himself				
2. window				
3. sunlamp				
4. mistake				
5. gossip				

Fluency: Sentences

Please unzip the tent.	It is bedtime.	Play inside until dinner.
He made a mistake.	She will take a catnap.	Go to sleep after the show.
The kitten is under the mat.	Enter the contest.	Please open the window.
I will go to the dentist.	Eat some dinner.	I hope you enjoy the song.

Sentence Writing

Word Bank			
inside	picnic	after	bedtime
enjoy	subject	unzip	dinner
upset	problem	mistake	rabbit

Lesson 30

1. _____

2. _____

Read Passage — Passage 1   Go to page 230 and read *The Rascal*.

1. Who did they think was the rascal at first?

2. What was digging holes in the yard?

Read Passage — Passage 2   Go to page 233 and read *Sundecks*.

1. What can you lay on when on a sundeck?

2. What can you do if the sundeck is old and dark?